ROW, ROW, ROW

Each of these swimming swines has something in common with the two other pigs in the same row. For example, all the porkers in the top row across have their eyes closed. Look at the other rows across, down, and diagonally. What's the same in each row?

Answer on page 47.

A "LITTLE" UNDERSTANDING

Every clue in this puzzle is about a name or title with the word "LITTLE" in it. Write the word that completes each clue in the grid. The descriptions in parentheses are there to give you a "little" help.

ACROSS

2. Little ___ ___ ___ Horn (site of General Custer's famous battle)

4. "I'm a little ___ ___ ___ ___ ___ ___, short and stout . . ."

9. Another word for "little," ___ ___ ___ Willie Winkie (nursery rhyme character)

10. Little ___ ___ ___ ___ (Windsor McKay character)

11. *The Little* ___ ___ ___ ___ ___ ___ *That Could* (children's story)

13. *Little* ___ ___ ___ ___ ___ (famous novel by Louisa May Alcott)

15. The Little ___ ___ ___ ___ (royal cartoon character)

17. "Little Bo ___ ___ ___ ___ lost her sheep . . ."

18. Little ___ ___ ___ ___ (one of Robin's Merry Men)

21. *The Little* ___ ___ ___ ___ ___ ___ ___ (animated film based on Hans Christian Andersen tale)

22. Little ___ ___ ___ ___ ___ ___ (the Green Giant's partner)

23. Little ___ ___ ___ ___ (dinosaur from *The Land That Time Forgot*)

25. "Twinkle, Twinkle, Little ___ ___ ___ ___" (song)

27. "The little ___ ___ ___ laughed to see such sport . . ."

30. Little Tommy ___ ___ ___ ___ ___ ___ (nursery rhyme character)

31. *The Brave Little* ___ ___ ___ ___ ___ ___ ___ (animated children's film)

32. "___ ___ ___ ___ had a little lamb . . ."

DOWN

1. "Little Jack ___ ___ ___ ___ ___ ___ sat in a corner . . ."

2. "Little Boy ___ ___ ___ ___, come blow your horn . . ."

3. "Sugar and spice and everything nice" make up a little ___ ___ ___ ___

5. Little Orphan ___ ___ ___ ___ ___ (comic strip character)

6. "One little, ___ ___ ___ little, three little Indians . . ."

7. *Little* ___ ___ ___ (sequel to novel in 13 across)

8. ___ ___ ___ ___ ___ ___ ___ ___ Little (children's story fowl)

12. "Little Lucy ___ ___ ___ ___ ___ ___ ___" (children's rhyme)

14. The Little ___ ___ ___ ___ ___ ___ (constellation)

16. *The Little* ___ ___ ___ *Hen* (fowl in a children's story)

17. Three Little ___ ___ ___ ___ (fairy tale characters who outsmarted the wolf)

19. *Little Red Riding* ___ ___ ___ ___ (fairy tale)

20. "The Little ___ ___ ___ ___ ___ ___ ___ ___ Boy" (Christmas song)

21. "Little Miss ___ ___ ___ ___ ___ ___ sat on a tuffet . . ."

22. ___ ___ ___ ___ ___ ___ *Little* (children's story by E. B. White)

24. Little ___ ___ ___ ___ (capital of Arkansas)

26. "Lil' ___ ___ ___ ___ ___" (comic strip)

28. "Put a little ___ ___ ___ into it." (coach's advice to pitcher)

29. Little ___ ___ (nickname of tennis champion Maureen Connolly)

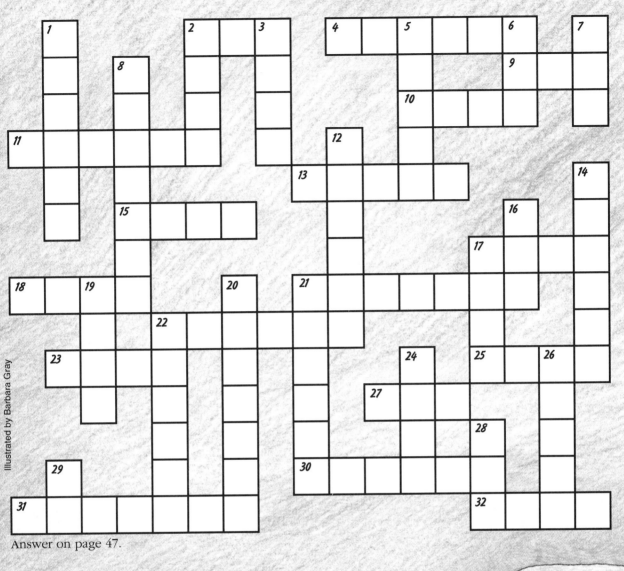

Illustrated by Barbara Gray

Answer on page 47.

DINERSAURS

Although many dinosaurs may look big and ferocious, only a few actually ate meat, while the rest were vegetarians. Can you identify which of these dinosaurs were carnivores (meat eaters) and which were herbivores (plant eaters)?

1. Tyrannosaurus
2. Pteranodon
3. Corythosaurus
4. Megalosaurus
5. Plesiosaurus
6. Stegosaurus
7. Ceratopsian
8. Saurolophus
9. Diplodocus
10. Apatosaurus
11. Edaphosaurus
12. Mosasaurus
13. Triceratops
14. Ankylosaurus

Answer on page 47.

DOT MAGIC

Connect these dots to see someone preparing for a big leap.

HIDDEN PICTURES

There are at least 17 objects hidden in this scene. How many can you find?

BACKTRACKS

Can you tell which tiny truck belongs at which small garage?

A

C

B

D

E

Illustrated by Patrick Girouard

Answer on page 47.

WHICH DOES NOT COMPUTE?

Circle the one equation that doesn't belong in each row across.

A. 6 + 2   3 + 5   7 + 3   4 + 4

B. 10 ÷ 2   3 + 3   4 + 1   10 − 5

C. 10 − 3   6 + 1   4 + 3   5 + 3

D. 8 + 3   2 x 3   12 ÷ 2   3 + 3

E. 2 x 5   6 + 5   5 + 5   12 − 2

F. 3 x 6   6 x 2   10 + 2   8 + 4

G. 4 + 5   10 − 1   5 + 5   8 + 1

H. 3 + 8   15 − 4   16 − 5   2 x 6

I. 11 − 7   5 + 2   2 x 2   3 + 1

J. 9 ÷ 3   3 x 1   8 − 4   6 − 3

Answer on page 47.

TWO ZOOS

There are two zoos on these pages. One holds animals in English; the other holds the same animals in Spanish. Look up, down, across, backward, and diagonally to find them all. The animals will not be hidden in the same places in both zoos. The words in parentheses are not part of the puzzle, but will tell you how to pronounce the names of the animals in Spanish.

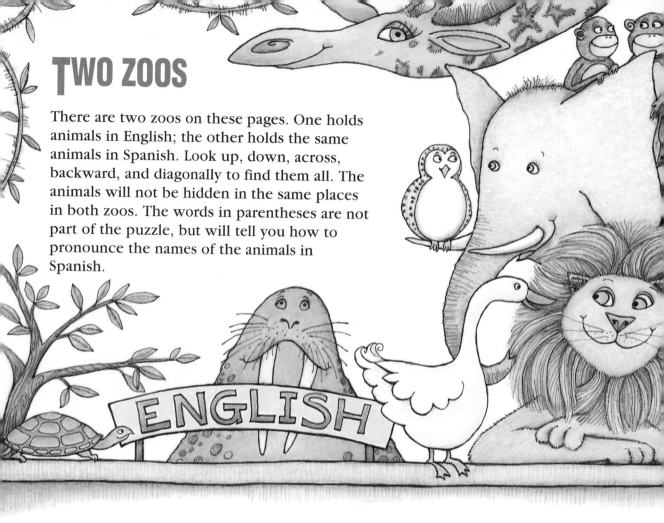

ENGLISH

```
E  K  A  N  S  D  A  O  T
O  L  Y  W  U  T  A  C  Z
S  I  E  C  X  O  Y  E  R
T  O  K  P  L  R  B  Z  E
R  N  N  W  H  R  A  T  V
I  L  O  V  A  A  A  Q  A
C  A  M  E  L  P  N  E  E
H  E  D  R  E  G  I  T  B
O  S  P  R  E  Y  M  Z  A
```

ELEPHANT
OSTRICH
MONKEY
BEAVER
OSPREY
PARROT
SNAKE
CAMEL
ZEBRA
TIGER
TOAD
LION
BEAR
DUCK
SEAL
OWL
RAT
CAT

Illustrated by Liisa Chauncy Guida

ELEFANTE (ele-fante)
AVESTRUZ (ahvey-strooz)
MONO (moan-oh)
CASTOR (cah-storr)
GARZA (gar-zah)
PAPAGAYO (pah-pah-gah-yo)
CULEBRA (coo-lay-brah)
CAMELLO (cah-meh-yo)
CEBRA (ce-vra)
TIGRE (tee-gray)
SAPO (sah-poh)
LEON (lay-ohn)
OSO (oh-so)
PATO (pah-toe)
FOCA (foh-ka)
MOCHUELO (moh-chew-ello)
RATA (rah-ta)
GATO (gah-toe)

```
M  O  N  O  G  A  R  Z  A
O  L  Y  T  T  W  T  V  R
C  L  X  A  O  I  E  O  B
H  E  R  P  G  S  T  F  E
U  M  Q  R  T  A  O  O  C
E  A  E  R  G  L  P  C  S
L  C  U  L  E  B  R  A  S
O  Z  R  O  T  S  A  C  A  P  O
E  T  N  A  F  E  L  E  O
```

Answer on page 48.

OCCUPATIONAL VIEWS

Each view on these pages is what someone might see while they are at work. For example, the first view is what a sewer worker might see. Can you guess the occupation of the person who is seeing each sight?

1 _____

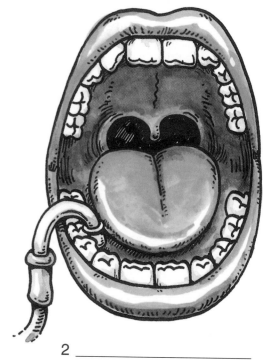

2 _____

3 _____

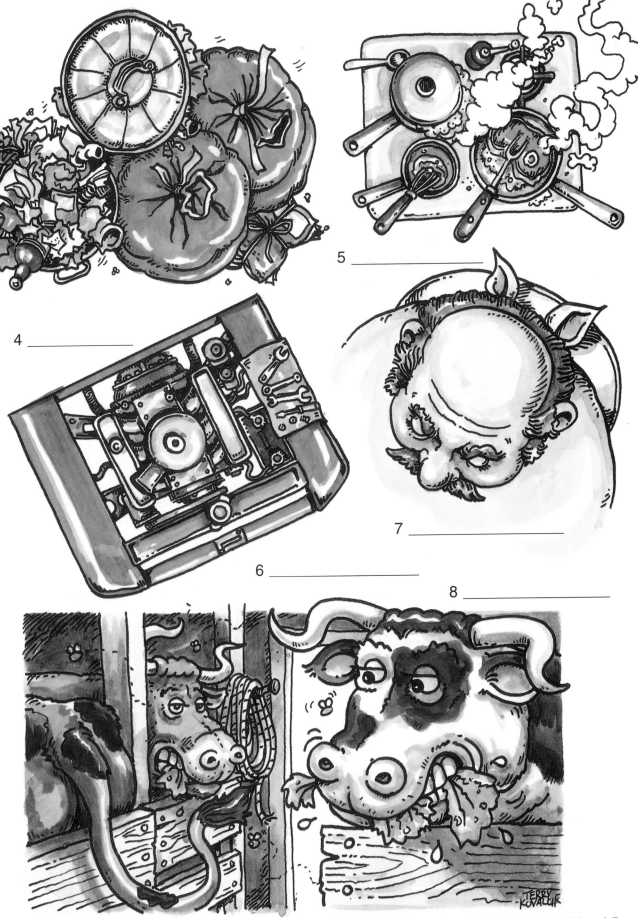

5 _____

4 _____

7 _____

6 _____

8 _____

Answer on page 48.

BY THE LIGHT OF THE SILVERY MOON

How many differences can you find between these two pictures?

INSTANT PICTURE

Fill in each section that contains two dots to get a spectacular view.

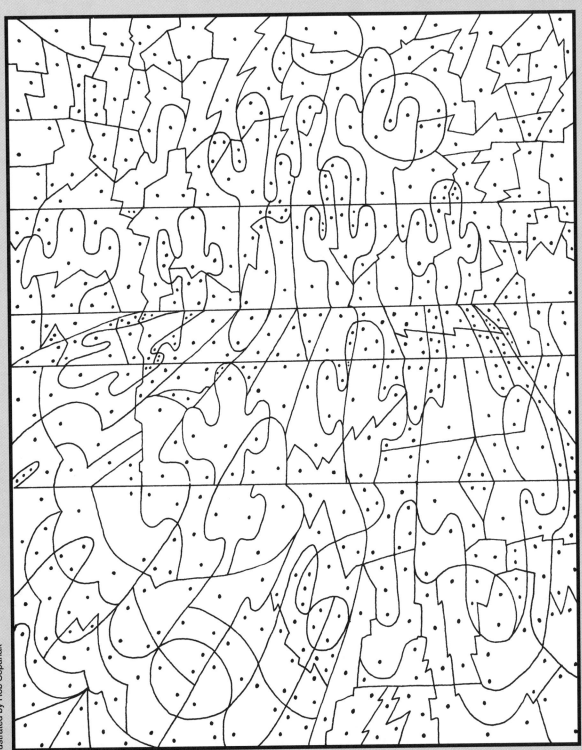

Answer on page 48.

GLOBE PROBE

Every letter of the alphabet can be placed in the lines below so that when completed, the names of 26 countries will be revealed, one country on each line. The letters you fill in may come at the beginning, middle, or end of the names. Each letter will be used only once. Not all the letters in each row of the chart will be used. Cincinnati Holmes has already filled in the first two examples. Can you do the others?

A B C D E F G H I J K L M N O P Q R S T U V W X Y Z

P O S W **E** D E N S N

E I D E **J** A P A N A

V E N N ___ R W A Y T

R F A I ___ A L Y E J

C K E N ___ A R U S S

E C H A ___ T H S O W

H E P A ___ I S T A N

T H R O ___ A T A R I

B O T S ___ A N A W A

F R A E ___ U A D O R

L C H I ___ E O L C O

S W E I ___ R A E L E

D E V M ___ L I E T H

R U C H ___ N A N T O

P P E R ___ J A I T P

D E I S ___ R A N C E

B E G Y ___ T E Z I L

E X L I ___ R A Z I L

B I G E ___ M A N Y N

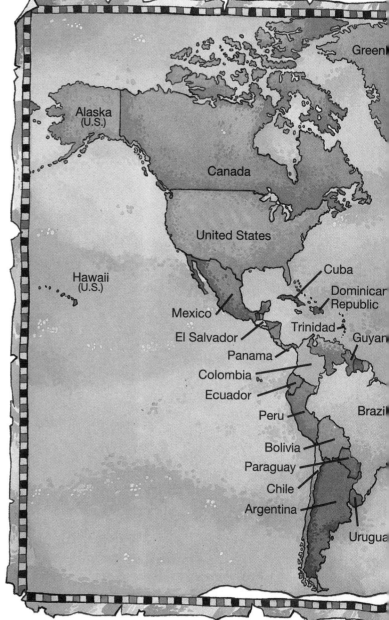

Greenl

Alaska
(U.S.)

Canada

United States

Hawaii
(U.S.)

Cuba

Dominican
Republic

Mexico

El Salvador

Trinidad

Guyan

Panama

Colombia

Ecuador

Brazi

Peru

Bolivia

Paraguay

Chile

Argentina

Urugua

Illustrated by John Nez

L O E T __ I O P I A

J T A N __ A N I A W

Q U M E __ I C O R N

Q U A N __ O L A R G

T U C A __ A D A M L

B O L I __ I A R O S

M O Z A __ B I Q U E

DENTAL DIFFICULTY

Jill had seven patients for dental exams today. When she started to do her summary for the day, she found that she had left her appointment book at work. Read what Jill remembers below and help her place each person's first and last names at the correct time of their appointment.

1. Clara came right after lunch, which was at noon. She was after Mr. Owen.
2. Mrs. Lesser was second.
3. Miss Hunt came in between Anita Hayes and John.
4. Melvin was right before lunch.
5. Mrs. Hayes only took half an hour.
6. Matt Lesser came before his wife, Elaine.
7. Clara's daughter was right after her.
8. Mr. Daniels was last, after Amy.

9:00 _____

10:00 _____

11:00 _____

12:30 _____

1:00 _____

2:00 _____

3:00 _____

Answer on page 48.

Illustrated by Rich Johnson

ALCHEMICAL REACTION

Alchemy was the ancient science that tried to turn lead into gold. By using the steps laid out here, see if you can perform some alchemy to turn lead into gold. Change only one letter at each step to form a new word.

LEAD

___ ___ ___ ___ Scan a book

___ ___ ___ ___ Path or street

___ ___ ___ ___ Tease or dare someone into doing something

GOLD

Now try these other changes.

CAT

___ ___ ___ Foldaway bed

___ ___ ___ Small point

DOG

KING

___ ___ ___ ___ Wedding band

___ ___ ___ ___ Sounded the bell

___ ___ ___ ___ Level in a group

___ ___ ___ ___ Place for tapes or spices

JACK

BOOK

___ ___ ___ ___ Prepare food

___ ___ ___ ___ Not warm

___ ___ ___ ___ Energy source for cookouts

___ ___ ___ ___ Baby horse

___ ___ ___ ___ Top of waves or root beer

___ ___ ___ ___ Wander about aimlessly

___ ___ ___ ___ Measure of paper

READ

WELCOME HOME

Before they went out this morning, your parents put you in charge. But your little brother's friends came over and made quite a mess.

Look closely at the "Before" picture. It shows the living room the way your parents left it. Can you find 15 changes in the way the room looks "Now"?

Before

Illustrated by Tim Ellis

Now

WHO AM I?

To find the name of a famous general who later became president of the United States, answer each of the questions below. Write each answer downward in the boxes. When you have completed the puzzle, a person's name will appear in the yellow boxes.

Down only:

1. General Lee surrendered to him at Appomattox _____ House in Virginia.
2. He fought "The War between the States," which is better known as "The _____ War."
3. His wife, Julia, four sons, and one daughter made up his _____.
4. He loved _____, and as soon as he learned to walk, he learned to ride.
5. The _____ was called the Gray because of the color of their uniforms.
6. During his presidency, Alexander Graham _____ invented the telephone.
7. His parents, Jesse and Hannah, named their eldest _____ Hiram. He is better known by his middle name.
8. During his civilian life, he had become a partner in a real _____ agency.
9. He was the first man to hold the rank of full _____ since George Washington.
10. As a child he worked on the family _____, taking care of the animals.
11. He was born on the 27th day of _____ (4th month) in 1822 in Point Pleasant, Ohio.
12. During the Civil War, President _____ had a great deal of confidence in him.
13. He attended the military academy at West _____.

Answer on page 48.

DISH DESIGN

This dish needs a design before it's ready to hang on the wall.
Use your imagination to put on a face, a handprint, some spin art,
or anything else you might like.

Jennifer
Fink

STATE SECRET

On February 20, 1792, the U.S. Postal Service was established, and now letters can be sent all across the United States in a matter of days. Look at the outline of the state below each space. Then find that state on the map on the next page and look for the letter inside it. Place the letter in the corresponding space to answer the riddle at the bottom.

Why must envelopes be so strong?

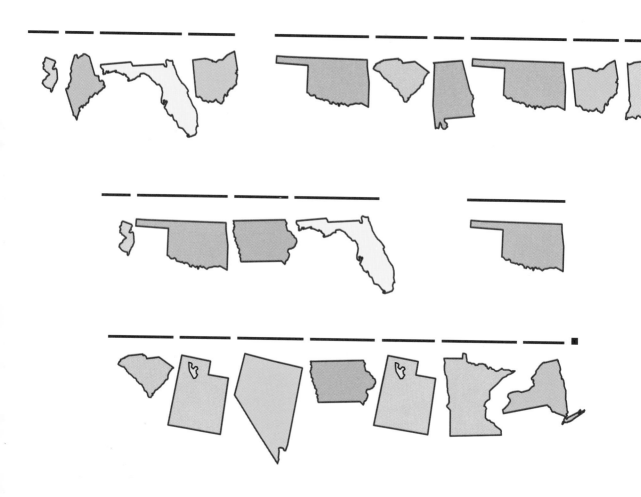

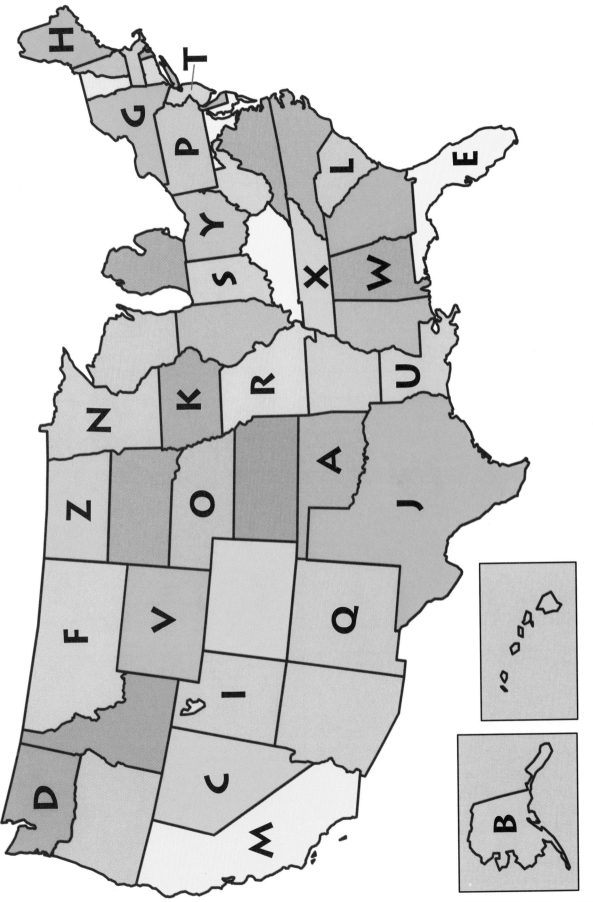

Illustrated by Steve Mantinaos

Answer on page 49.

CUTTING IT CLOSE

Number these pictures to show what happened first, second, and so on.

Answer on page 49.

WITH OPEN ARMS

You'll get a WARM feeling if you can complete each word that has A-R-M in it.

1. crop land: ___ ARM

2. injure: ___ ARM

3. group of soldiers: ARM ___

4. knight's metal suit: ARM ___ ___

5. locket or bracelet piece: ___ ___ ARM

6. gentle heat: ___ ARM ___ ___

7. piece of clothing: ___ ARM ___ ___ ___

8. pesty animal: ___ ARM ___ ___ ___

9. drugstore: ___ ___ ARM ___ ___ ___

10. protective ear coverings: ___ ARM ___ ___ ___ ___

11. small wind instrument: ___ ARM ___ ___ ___ ___

12. common mint or gum flavor: ___ ___ ___ ARM ___ ___ ___

13. jelly: ___ ARM ___ ___ ___ ___ ___

14. bony-plated animal: ARM ___ ___ ___ ___ ___ ___

Answer on page 49.

PICTURE MIXER

Copy these mixed-up squares in the spaces on the next page to put this picture back together. The letters and numbers tell you where each square belongs. The first one, A-3, has been done for you.

A-3 A-2 A-1 A-4
B-1 B-3 B-4 B-2
C-2 C-3 C-1 C-4
D-1 D-4 D-2 D-3

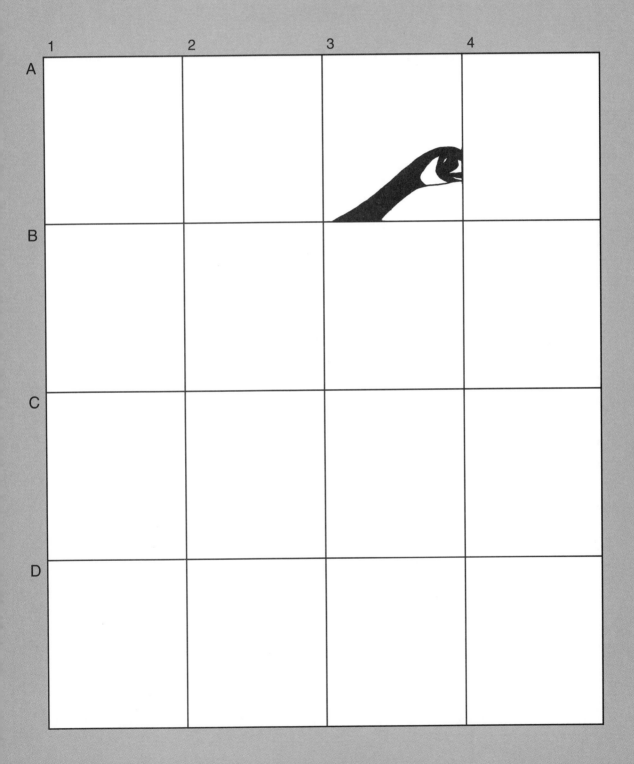

	1	2	3	4
A				
B				
C				
D				

BACK AT THE RANCH

How many unusual things can you find in this picture?

Illustrated by John Nez

STOP, LOOK, AND LIST

Under every category, list one thing that begins with each letter. For example, one bird that begins with "S" is Swan. See if you can name another.

BIRDS

S _____

R _____

W _____

H _____

T _____

TOOLS

S _____

R _____

W _____

H _____

T _____

COMIC BOOK SUPERHEROES

S _____

R _____

W _____

H _____

T _____

Illustrated by Lisa Dayer

Answer on page 49.

AN AQUATIC QUESTION

Can you answer the crab's question? Follow the directions on page 35 to find the letters you need. To answer the riddle, put each letter in all the correct spaces. For example, put letter number one in each space with the numeral 1 below it.

$\underline{}\ \underline{}\quad\underline{}\ \underline{}\ \underline{}\ \underline{}\ \underline{}\quad\underline{}\ \underline{}\ \underline{}\ \underline{}$.
1 2   3 4 5 1 6   7 8 9 3

How do underwater police officers get around?

Illustrated by Lynn Adams

Letter number one is sticking out of the sand on the left.

In the treasure chest lies the fifth letter.

The clam is holding letter six, while the shark has the ninth.

Watch out for the ray, who has a false letter.

The sea horse's letter is a phony, but the starfish has the real second letter.

Dive way down below the kelp to find letter number eight.

Explore the sunken wreck. The fourth letter is in the porthole.

The seventh letter is lower on the wheel.

Be very quiet. The sleeping baby holds letter three.

TUBE TEST

Doctor Karloff has lost all his test tubes. How many can you find?

WHAT'S IN A WORD?

We've been struggling to find as many words as possible in the letters of WRESTLING. Each word has to be three letters or more, and none can be plurals ending in "S." If you can find at least 60 words, you're the WRESTLING champ.

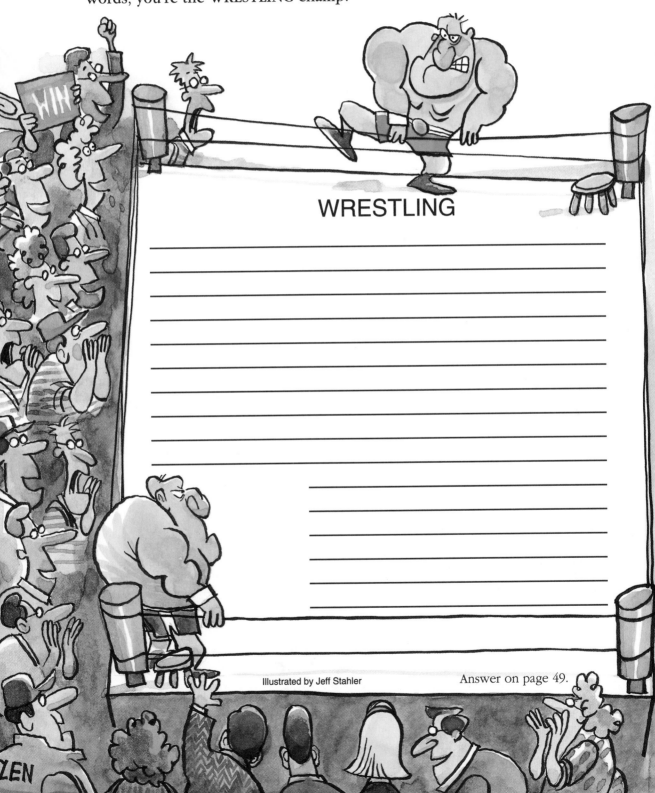

WRESTLING

Illustrated by Jeff Stahler

Answer on page 49.

SYMBOLS & SIGNS

These symbols may look familiar, but
can you fit their everyday meanings
into the right places in the grid?
Hint: if you need help recognizing
each symbol, there is a word list
on page 50.

Across	Down
1. "	2. #
7. " "	3. ?
8. ÷	4. '
9. =	5. -
10. @	6. ,
12. <	8. $
13. £	11. ¢
14. ¶	14. %
17. >	15. *
18. ℅	16. √
19. .	19. π
20. w/	
21. §	

Answer on page 49.

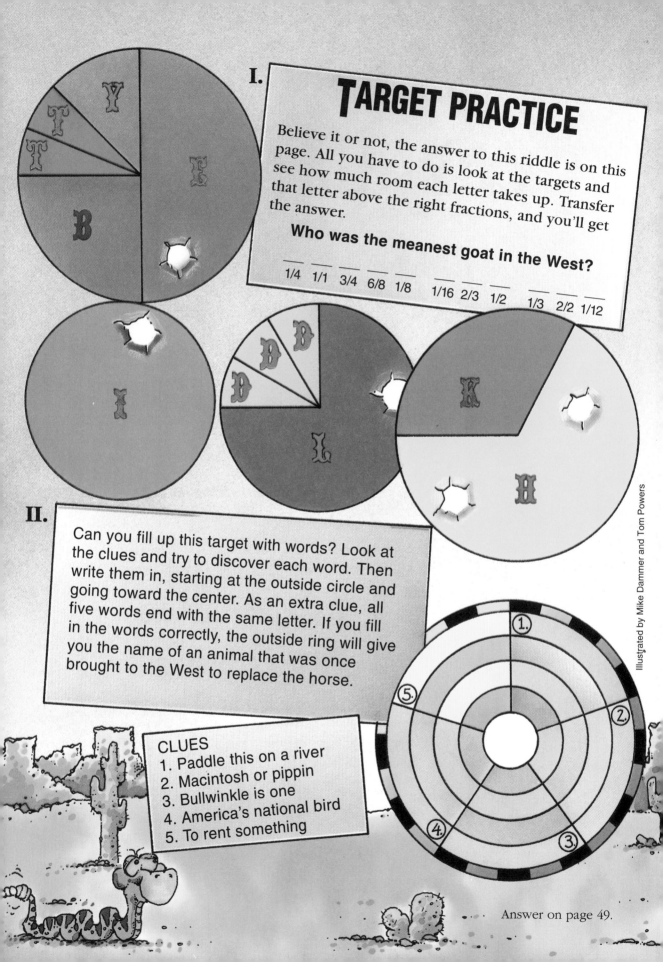

I.

TARGET PRACTICE

Believe it or not, the answer to this riddle is on this page. All you have to do is look at the targets and see how much room each letter takes up. Transfer that letter above the right fractions, and you'll get the answer.

Who was the meanest goat in the West?

—— —— —— —— ——   —— —— ——   —— —— ——
1/4 1/1 3/4 6/8 1/8   1/16 2/3 1/2   1/3 2/2 1/12

II.

Can you fill up this target with words? Look at the clues and try to discover each word. Then write them in, starting at the outside circle and going toward the center. As an extra clue, all five words end with the same letter. If you fill in the words correctly, the outside ring will give you the name of an animal that was once brought to the West to replace the horse.

CLUES
1. Paddle this on a river
2. Macintosh or pippin
3. Bullwinkle is one
4. America's national bird
5. To rent something

Illustrated by Mike Dammer and Tom Powers

Answer on page 49.

SAFARI MEMORIES

Take a long look at this picture. Try to remember everything you see in it. Then turn the page and answer some questions without looking back at the picture.

Illustrated by Jon Davis

DON'T READ THIS UNTIL YOU HAVE LOOKED AT "Safari Memories—Part I" ON PAGE 41.

SAFARI MEMORIES
Part II

Can you answer these questions about the scene you saw? Don't peek!

1. What did the white sign say?
2. Were there more monkeys or lions in the picture?
3. What color car was being overrun?
4. How many automobiles could be seen?
5. Was any human wearing a mustache?
6. How many male lions were present?
7. Was any car carrying luggage?
8. What kinds of buildings were in the background?

Answer on page 50.

DOMINO DILEMMA

Arrange these five dominoes within the pattern pictured below so that a correct addition problem is shown. The dots on each half-domino represent a one-digit number. For example, a half with three dots equals the number 3.

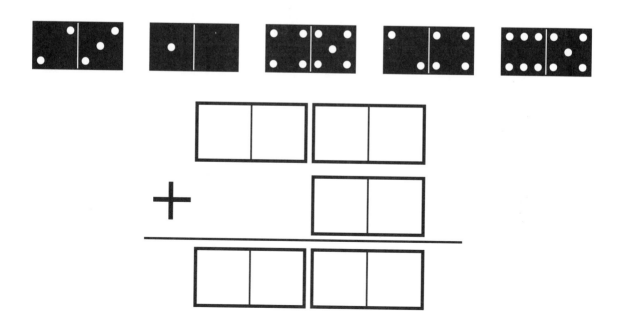

Answer on page 50.

PLACE A LETTER

Each set of two words can be turned into one longer word
when you add a missing letter. None of the missing letters
are the same, but you should be able to find them all.

A B C D E F G H I J K L M N O P Q R S T U V W X Y Z

1. POT ___ TOES

2. FORE ___ ONE

3. HI ___ DEN

4. CAR ___ RIDGE

5. PIG ___ ON

6. FIN ___ SHED

7. NEW ___ PAPER

8. BASE ___ ALL

9. NAP ___ IN

10. KIT ___ HEN

11. BE ___ ORE

12. TOOT ___ PICK

Answer on page 50.

QUEST FOR THE HOLY GRAIL

The Amazing Mazers hadn't been in merry olde England long
when they came across a knight crying by the side of the road.
This knight was so sad even his horse was crying!

"What's wrong, good knight?" Millie asked.

"Ah, fair maiden, I am Percy, the knight of the Woeful
Countenance. Without disturbing any of the sleeping ogres,
I must find the keys that will open the doors along the one
path which leads to the Holy Grail."

"Holy cow!" said Max.

"No, Holy Grail," the knight repeated.
"Weren't you listening?"

"Perhaps we can help," Millie offered.

Can you help the Mazers get to the
castle without waking any ogres?
Along the way search for the hidden
keys that open the doors leading
to the Holy Grail.

Answer on page 50.

Illustrated by Charles Jordan

JUMBLED GYM

The kids want to have fun in the playground, but somebody jumbled up all the equipment. Unscramble each word to get something you might find on a playground.

DELIS

WINGS

ESEWAS

LACEROUS

SHART ANCS

KONYEM RABS

GRINS

STOPCHOCH

BLATHERTEL

LALBS

ROSHES

BANXSOD

PUJM EPOR

LINCHERD

Illustrated by Terry Rogers

Answer on page 50.

ANSWERS

COVER

ROW, ROW, ROW (page 3)

polka dots   fish   splashes   sunglasses

eyes closed

tails

open mouths

fins

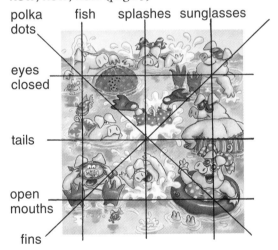

A "LITTLE" UNDERSTANDING (pages 4-5)

DINERSAURS (page 6)

1. Tyrannosaurus–meat eater
2. Pteranodon–meat eater
3. Corythosaurus–plant eater
4. Megalosaurus–meat eater
5. Plesiosaurus–meat eater
6. Stegosaurus–plant eater
7. Ceratopsian–meat eater
8. Saurolophus–plant eater
9. Diplodocus–plant eater
10. Apatosaurus–plant eater
11. Edaphosaurus–meat eater
12. Mosasaurus–meat eater
13. Triceratops–plant eater
14. Ankylosaurus–plant eater

DOT MAGIC (page 7)

BACKTRACKS (page 10)

A–3
B–1
C–4
D–2
E–5

WHICH DOES NOT COMPUTE? (page 11)

A. 7 + 3	F. 3 x 6
B. 3 + 3	G. 5 + 5
C. 5 + 3	H. 2 x 6
D. 8 + 3	I. 5 + 2
E. 6 + 5	J. 8 – 4

TWO ZOOS (pages 12-13)

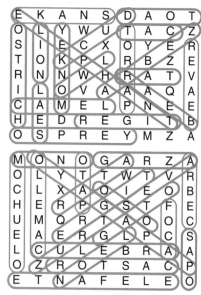

OCCUPATIONAL VIEWS (pages 14-15)

1. Sewer worker
2. Dentist
3. Bus driver
4. Sanitation worker
5. Chef
6. Mechanic
7. Barber
8. Farmer

INSTANT PICTURE (page 17)

GLOBE PROBE (pages 18-19)

PO**SWEDEN**SN
EIDE**JAPAN**A
VEN**NORWAY**T
RFA**ITALY**EJ
C**KENYA**RUSS
E**CHAD**THSOW
HE**PAKISTAN**
THRO**QATAR**I
BOTSWANAWA
FRA**ECUADOR**
L**CHILE**OLCO
SWE**ISRAEL**E
DEV**MALI**ETH

RU**CHINA**NTO
P**PERU**JAITP
DEIS**FRANCE**
BE**GYPT**EZIL
EXLI**BRAZIL**
BI**GERMANY**N
LO**ETHIOPIA**
J**TANZANIA**W
QU**MEXICO**RN
QU**ANGOLA**RG
TU**CANADA**ML
BOLIVIAROS
MOZAMBIQUE

DENTAL DIFFICULTY (page 20)

9:00—Matt Lesser
10:00—Elaine Lesser
11:00—Melvin Owen
12:30—Clara Hayes
1:00—Anita Hayes
2:00—Amy Hunt
3:00—John Daniels

ALCHEMICAL REACTION (page 21)

LEAD	CAT	KING	BOOK
READ	COT	RING	COOK
ROAD	DOT	RANG	COOL
GOAD	DOG	RANK	COAL
GOLD		RACK	FOAL
		JACK	FOAM
			ROAM
			REAM
			READ

WELCOME HOME (pages 22-23)

1. The throw rug is in a different position.
2. There is a toy truck under the throw rug.
3. The picture of the woman is crooked.
4. The lamp shade is also crooked.
5. There are footprints going across the floor.
6. The pattern on the couch doesn't match because a cushion has been moved.
7. One of the plants on the windowsill is tipped over, and there is a pile of dirt.
8. There is a dirty plate on the table.
9. Some books in the bookcase are falling over.
10. There is a ball in the bookcase.
11. The glass in the window is cracked.
12. The draperies have handprints on them.
13. The man in the picture now has a mustache.
14. There is a tricycle in the room.
15. There is a pile of coats on the floor.

WHO AM I? (page 24)

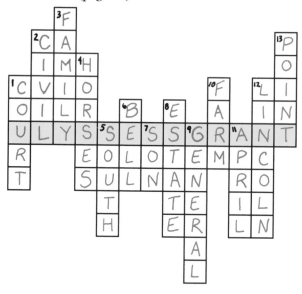

STATE SECRET (pages 26-27)
Why must envelopes be so strong?
They always take a licking.

CUTTING IT CLOSE (page 28)

5	4
2	6
3	1

WITH OPEN ARMS (page 29)

1. farm	8. varmint
2. harm	9. pharmacy
3. army	10. earmuffs
4. armor	11. harmonica
5. charm	12. spearmint
6. warmth	13. marmalade
7. garment	14. armadillo

PICTURE MIXER (pages 30-31)

STOP, LOOK, AND LIST (page 33)
Here are our answers. You may have found others

Birds	**Tools**
Sparrow	Screwdriver
Roadrunner	Rasp
Wren	Wretch
Hawk	Hammer
Thrush	Trowel

Comic Book Superheroes

Spider-Man	Hulk
Robin	Thor
Wonder Woman	

AN AQUATIC QUESTION (pages 34-35)
How do underwater police officers get around?
IN SQUID CARS.

WHAT'S IN A WORD? (page 37)

WRESTLING
We pinned down 88 words. You may have found others.

enlist	listen	sing	tin
gel	lit	singer	tine
get	liter	sir	tingle
glint	nest	sire	tinsel
glisten	new	siren	tire
grew	news	sit	twin
grin	Nile	site	twine
grist	rent	sling	twinge
grit	resign	sterling	west
insert	rest	stern	wet
ire	resting	stew	wig
isle	rile	sting	win
leg	ring	stinger	wine
lent	ringlet	stir	wing
let	rite	strew	winter
lie	set	strewn	wire
lier	sew	string	wise
line	sign	swine	wiser
liner	signet	swing	wren
linger	silent	tie	wring
lint	silt	tiger	wrist
list	sin	tile	write

SYMBOLS & SIGNS (pages 38-39)

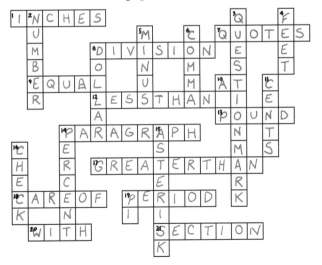

TARGET PRACTICE (page 40)
I. Who was the meanest goat in the west?
   Billy the Kid

II.
1. Canoe	3. Moose	5. Lease
2. Apple	4. Eagle	

Outside word: Camel

SAFARI MEMORIES (page 42)

1. Do not feed the elephants
2. Monkeys
3. Red
4. Four
5. No
6. Three
7. Yes
8. Snack Shop and Ranger Stand

DOMINO DILEMMA (page 42)

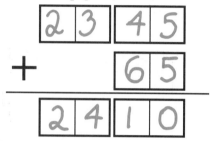

PLACE A LETTER (page 43)

1. A makes POTATOES
2. G makes FOREGONE
3. D mades HIDDEN
4. T makes CARTRIDGE
5. E makes PIGEON
6. I makes FINISHED
7. S makes NEWSPAPER
8. B makes BASEBALL
9. K makes NAPKIN
10. C makes KITCHEN
11. F makes BEFORE
12. H makes TOOTHPICK

JUMBLED GYM (page 46)

slide
swing
seesaw
carousel
trash cans
monkey bars
rings
hopscotch
tetherball
balls
horses
sandbox
jump rope
children

SYMBOLS AND SIGNS (pages 38-39)

HINT LIST: These words are listed alphabetically. It's up to you to match them all with the correct symbols on page 38.

asterisk	less than
at	minus
care of	number
cents	paragraph
check	percent
comma	period
division	pi
dollar	pound
equal	question
feet	quotes
greater than	section
inches	with

QUEST FOR THE HOLY GRAIL (pages 44-45)